The
Politically Correct
Night Before
Christmas

SWEETWATER
PRESS

The Politically Correct Night Before Christmas
Copyright © 2006
Produced by Cliff Road Books

ISBN-13: 978-1-58173-612-0
ISBN-10: 1-58173-612-6

Book by Anonymous
Book illustrated by Ernie Eldredge
Book design by Miles G. Parsons

Printed in Italy

The Politically Correct Night Before Christmas

by Anonymous
Illustrated by Ernie Eldredge

SWEETWATER
PRESS

'Twas the night before the generic holiday celebration...

And all through our multicultural, environmentally friendly, expertly feng shui'd house…

Not an animal rights activist was stirring,

unless it was to prevent the exploitation
of an innocent little mouse.

The union was hanging the stockings where they would not be a fire hazard or threaten anyone's equal gift-giving rights,

Nor would the gifts deposited therein affect election results on this or any other night.

The children were snuggled down without infringement on their option to choose a bedtime,

Dreaming freely of whatever on earth they wanted, regardless of reason, financial expenditure, or rhyme.

When out above the federally protected, highway beautifying, ozone-replenishing trees

Came a sound louder than a demonstration to protect the local endangered species!

I sprang out of bed and threw open the double-pane insulated, natural-wood window I built by hand,

And looked out over the solar panels and organic garden to our neighborhood association-managed land.

The moon was the brightest thing in sight since we don't support that price-gouging utility company,

And by its light I saw the most amazing hybrid-powered prototype vehicle flying by me!

With a little
ol' driver so inoffensive
and internationally arcane,

He could have been the ambassador to the
United Nations from any country you could name.

Eight ethnically diverse, politically neutral reindeer were escorting that rig,

Without incurring **OSHA** violations or unpaid overtime while working this gig.

If you don't mind, Dasher and Dancer!

"After you, Prancer and Vixen!

"Only if you want to, Comet and Cupid!

"I'd appreciate it so much, Donder and Blitzen!"

From the top of the blue states to the bottom of the red,
They flew toys not made in overseas sweat shops to kids asleep in their beds.

You know how everyone rushes in, disclaimers in hand,
Whenever an opinion is clearly expressed in this land?

Well that's how fast this holiday action committee flew,
Spreading joy without regard to race, creed, color, gender, or the religious affiliation of a few.

And then in a twinkling, I heard a polite tap at the door.
Could it be? Were they here to give us who have everything…even more?

I answered the door in two seconds flat.
There they were, thoughtfully wiping their feet on the mat!

They were dressed all in natural fiber from their heads to their feet,
And they entered assuring me no one would be left out on our street.

The generic holiday gentleman in charge
of this operation
Scurried around spending his grant money
to enhance our holiday celebration.

He confessed he used to smoke a pipe
clenched in his teeth,
But of course now there's a ban on smoke
encircling one's head like a wreath.

He said he used to put cookies, milk, and
everything else in his belly,
So it shook when he laughed, like a bowl
full of jelly.

No longer chubby and plump, now he runs
marathons in his spare time,
And he proclaimed he liked a high protein, low
fat, carb-concious, low glycemic diet just fine.

He gave a wink and a nod, then he
hastened to say
He hoped I wouldn't take that the wrong way.

(I wished he would hurry and fill up our stockings
Before the neighborhood gossips started talking!)

At last he finished his work and gave me a release to sign
Before I could rightfully call my gifts mine.

Don't read the small print," he said. "It's the standard stuff."
Then I signed, so he wouldn't go off in a huff.

But I heard him issue a statement as he drove out of sight:

"Happy Whatever to All, and to All a Good Night!"